ELEPHANT'S TUSK

Written by John Hare
Illustrated by Eva Gundersen

Hodder & Stoughton

When Elephant was very, very small,
his two little tusks grew much more
quickly than those of his friends.

And as he grew, they grew bigger . . .

And bigger . . .

Until one day his tusks were bigger than anyone else's. So the elephants gave him the name Toron Giwa, which means King of the Elephants.

But Elephant had two enemies.
One was a rival elephant called Marsabit.
He was jealous of Elephant and wanted
the title of Toron Giwa for himself.

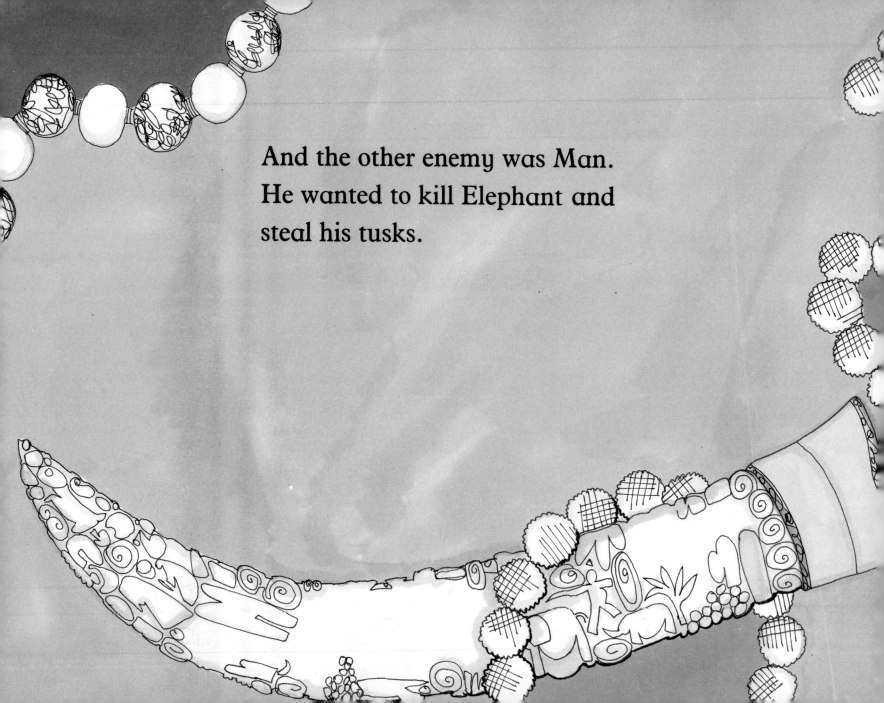

And the other enemy was Man.
He wanted to kill Elephant and
steal his tusks.

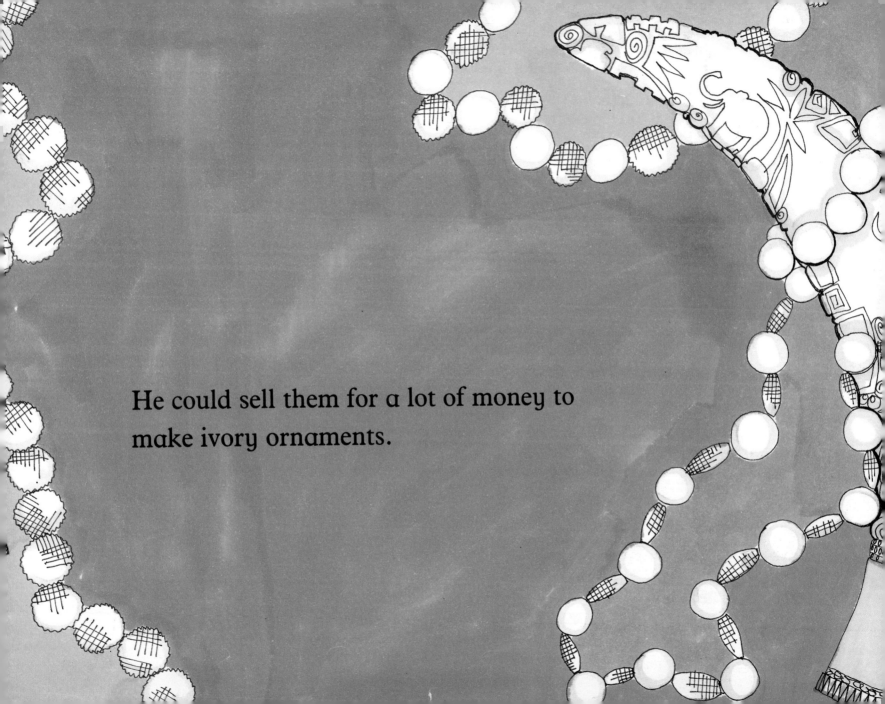

He could sell them for a lot of money to
make ivory ornaments.

One day Marsabit met Toron Giwa in the bush and challenged him to a fight.

So they charged each other with their huge
ears spread out in anger. The earth shook
with their bellows of rage and great trees were
snapped in half like matchsticks.

All the other elephants hid in fear and a great cloud of dust

rose high above the place where they were hiding.

The dust cloud showed Man where the elephants were. The birds tried to warn the elephants that he was coming to kill them.

The two elephants were still fighting each other and they did not see Man creeping up on them. But the monkeys did.

And Man raised his rifle and shot at Marsabit but he missed and the bullet went through his great flapping ear.

When Marsabit realised what had happened he stopped fighting Toron Giwa and the two elephants chased after Man with a great trumpeting and roaring.

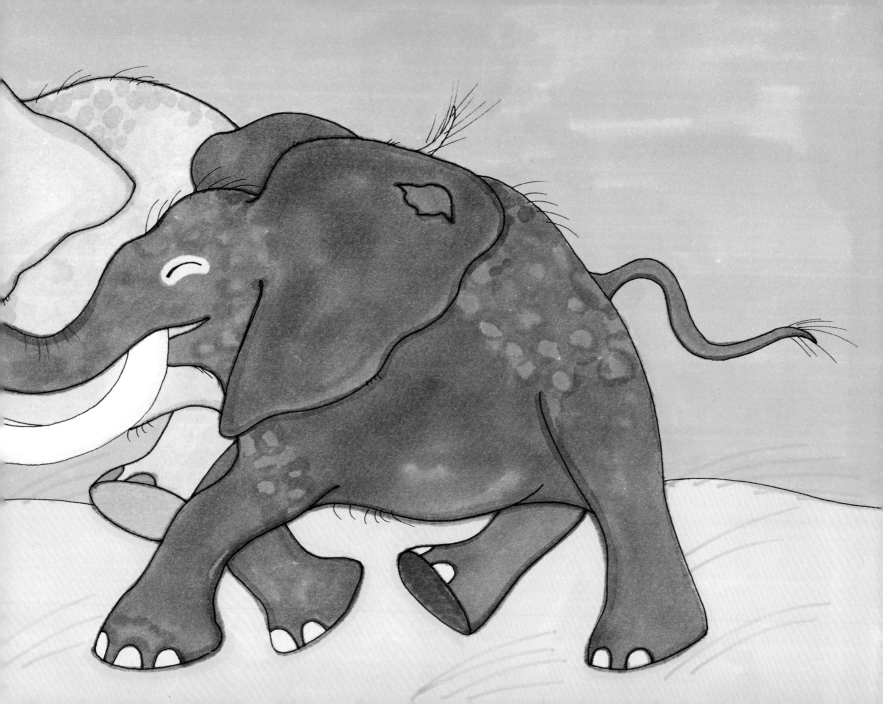

And when they had driven him right out of the bush, they shook trunks and agreed never to fight each other again.

They knew that
their only real enemy
was Man.

And more and more men are trying to kill elephants for their ivory tusks which they can sell for a great deal of money. So don't buy ivory and try to stop Man killing elephants because if you don't there will be

no more Marsabit
and no more Toron Giwa
and no more elephants – EVER

WWF

Note to parents from WWF:

We hope your child enjoys reading this book and learning about nature.

WWF has worked since 1961 to save not only animals, such as those in this book, but also the forests and wetlands and other habitats in which they live.

Your local WWF office can provide you with additional ways to inform your children about nature.

For Leon and
for Maile

ISBN 0-340-52399-9

First published 1990

Copyright © 1990 John Hare and Eva Gundersen

Photoset in Great Britain by Rowland Phototypesetting Limited, Bury St Edmunds, Suffolk.
Printed in Hong Kong for Hodder and Stoughton Educational, a division of Hodder and Stoughton Limited,
Mill Road, Dunton Green, Sevenoaks, Kent by Colorcraft Limited.